The Irish Get Up a...

ISBN 978-1-9...

Published in Ireland by
GET UP AND GO PUBLICATIONS LTD
Camboline, Hazelwood, Sligo, F91 NP04, Ireland.
Email: info@getupandgodiary.com
www.getupandgodiary.com

Compiled by Eileen Forrestal
Graphic design by Nuala Redmond
Illustrations: dreamstime.com; shutterstock.com
Printed in Ireland by GPS Colour Graphics.

The world is full of magic things, patiently waiting for our senses to grow sharper.

William Butler Yeats

Copyright c 2007-2023 Get Up And Go Publications Ltd.

All rights reserved. No part of this publication may be reproduced, stored in, or introduced into, a retrieval system, or transmitted in any form, or by any means (electronic, mechanical, scanning, recording or otherwise) without the prior permission of the Publisher. Any person who does any unauthorised act in relation to this publication may be liable to criminal prosecution and civil claim for damages.

2023 BANK AND PUBLIC HOLIDAYS

REPUBLIC OF IRELAND
New Year's Day, 2 January;
St Patrick's Day, 17 March;
Easter Monday, 10 April;
June Bank Holiday, 5 June;
October Bank Holiday, 30 October;
St Stephen's Day, 26 December.

St Brigid's Day, 6 February
Good Friday, 7 April;
May Day Bank Holiday, 1 May;
August Bank Holiday, 7 August;
Christmas Day, 25 December;

NORTHERN IRELAND
New Year's Day, 2 January;
Good Friday, 7 April;
May Day Holiday, 1 May;
Orangemen's Holiday, 12 July;
Christmas Day, 25 December;

St Patrick's Day, 17 March;
Easter Monday, 10 April;
Spring Bank Holiday, 29 May;
Summer Bank Holiday, 28 August;
Boxing Day, 26 December.

ENGLAND, SCOTLAND AND WALES
New Year's Day, 2 January;
Easter Monday, 10 April;
May Day Holiday, 1 May;
Summer Bank Holiday, 28 August;
Christmas Day, 25 December;

Good Friday, 7 April;
St George's Day, 23 April
Spring Bank Holiday, 29 May;
Remembrance Sunday, 12 November;
Boxing Day, 26 December.

UNITED STATES OF AMERICA
New Year's Day, 2 January;
Presidents' Day, 20 February;
Independence Day, 4 July;
Columbus Day, 9 October;
Thanksgiving Day, 23 November;

Martin Luther King Day, 16 January;
Memorial Day, 29 May;
Labour Day, 4 September;
Veterans Day, 10 November;
Christmas Day, 25 December.

CANADA
New Year's Day, 2 January;
Heritage Day, 20 February;
St Patrick's Day, 17 March;
Easter Monday, 10 April;
Canada Day, 1 July;
Thanksgiving Day, 9 October;
Christmas Day, 25 December;

Family Day, 20 February;
Commonwealth Day, 13 March;
Good Friday, 7 April;
Victoria Day 22 May;
Labour Day, 4 September;
Rememberance Day, 11 November;
Boxing Day, 26 December.

AUSTRALIA (NATIONAL HOLIDAYS)
New Year's Day, 2 January;
Good Friday, 7 April;
Anzac Day 25 April;
Christmas Day, 25 December;

Australia Day, 26 January;
Easter Monday, 10 April;
Queen's Birthday, 12 June;
Boxing Day, 26 December.

2023

JANUARY

Sun	Mon	Tue	Wed	Thu	Fri	Sat
1	2	3	4	5	6	7
8	9	10	11	12	13	14
15	16	17	18	19	20	21
22	23	24	25	26	27	28
29	30	31				

FEBRUARY

Sun	Mon	Tue	Wed	Thu	Fri	Sat
			1	2	3	4
5	6	7	8	9	10	11
12	13	14	15	16	17	18
19	20	21	22	23	24	25
26	27	28				

MARCH

Sun	Mon	Tue	Wed	Thu	Fri	Sat
			1	2	3	4
5	6	7	8	9	10	11
12	13	14	15	16	17	18
19	20	21	22	23	24	25
26	27	28	29	30	31	

APRIL

Sun	Mon	Tue	Wed	Thu	Fri	Sat
						1
2	3	4	5	6	7	8
9	10	11	12	13	14	15
16	17	18	19	20	21	22
23	24	25	26	27	28	29
30						

MAY

Sun	Mon	Tue	Wed	Thu	Fri	Sat
	1	2	3	4	5	6
7	8	9	10	11	12	13
14	15	16	17	18	19	20
21	22	23	24	25	26	27
28	29	30	31			

JUNE

Sun	Mon	Tue	Wed	Thu	Fri	Sat
				1	2	3
4	5	6	7	8	9	10
11	12	13	14	15	16	17
18	19	20	21	22	23	24
25	26	27	28	29	30	

JULY

Sun	Mon	Tue	Wed	Thu	Fri	Sat
						1
2	3	4	5	6	7	8
9	10	11	12	13	14	15
16	17	18	19	20	21	22
23	24	25	26	27	28	29
30	31					

AUGUST

Sun	Mon	Tue	Wed	Thu	Fri	Sat
		1	2	3	4	5
6	7	8	9	10	11	12
13	14	15	16	17	18	19
20	21	22	23	24	25	26
27	28	29	30	31		

SEPTEMBER

Sun	Mon	Tue	Wed	Thu	Fri	Sat
					1	2
3	4	5	6	7	8	9
10	11	12	13	14	15	16
17	18	19	20	21	22	23
24	25	26	27	28	29	30

OCTOBER

Sun	Mon	Tue	Wed	Thu	Fri	Sat
1	2	3	4	5	6	7
8	9	10	11	12	13	14
15	16	17	18	19	20	21
22	23	24	25	26	27	28
29	30	31				

NOVEMBER

Sun	Mon	Tue	Wed	Thu	Fri	Sat
			1	2	3	4
5	6	7	8	9	10	11
12	13	14	15	16	17	18
19	20	21	22	23	24	25
26	27	28	29	30		

DECEMBER

Sun	Mon	Tue	Wed	Thu	Fri	Sat
					1	2
3	4	5	6	7	8	9
10	11	12	13	14	15	16
17	18	19	20	21	22	23
24	25	26	27	28	29	30
31						

Forgive the past – let it go
Live the present – the power of now
Create the future – thoughts become things

Dear Reader,

We are delighted that you're holding this Get Up and Go diary in your hands today. You are about to embark on a wonderful journey with 'the world's best loved transformational diary'.

Whether this is your first Get Up and Go diary or you're a regular and loyal customer, we thank you, and we trust that you will benefit from the carefully chosen words contained herein.

You may have chosen this diary for yourself or received it as gift from a friend; either way, we know it will fill your days with inspiration, encouragement, motivation and empowerment in the year ahead.

You may also like to follow us on Facebook, Twitter and Instagram for additional timely words of inspiration and encouragement. Please check out our website **www.getupandgodiary.com** where you can find out about (and purchase) new products, follow our blog, **subscribe to our newsletter**, learn about upcoming events and see details of special offers.

Also there's something extra we think you'll appreciate. Through our partnership with the Global Giving Initiative **www.B1G1.com** this diary is changing lives – a contribution from each diary becomes a 'Giving Impact' in support of a worthy cause in the developing world. You'll see more about all of that on our website.

And it all happens because people like you love their Get Up and Go diary. Thank you so much for being one of them.

We are delighted to say we are now sourcing our paper from FSC. FSC certification ensures that products come from responsibly managed forests that provide environmental, social and economic benefits. And ... we have been named "Allstar Inspirational Diary of the Year"!

Thank you for your support.

With very best wishes for the year ahead,

from the Get Up and Go team

This diary belongs to: _____

Address: _____

Tel: _____   Email: _____

Emergency telephone number: _____

Discipline is the bridge between goals and accomplishments.

spriocanna

GOALS

EANÁIR
JANUARY

Is ait an mac an saol.

Life is strange.

Tá onóir ag an aois agus uaisle ag an óige.

Age is honorable and youth is noble.

January

20 23

Nothing in life is to be feared, only understood. It is now the time to understand more, so that we fear less.

Marie Curie

The object of a New Year is not that we should have a new year. It is that we should have a new soul.

GK Chesterson

If you cry because the sun has gone out of your life, your tears will prevent you from seeing the stars.

Tagore

My will shall shape the future. Whether I fail or succeed, shall be no one's doing but my own. I am the force; I can clear any obstacle before me, or get lost in the maze. My choice. My responsibility. Win or lose, only I hold the key to my destiny.

Elaine Maxwell

SUNDAY **1** HAPPY NEW YEAR!

Make a list of everything you have ever done

MONDAY 2 Bank holiday

Make a list of all you have yet to do

TUESDAY 3

Let go what doesn't serve you

*This new day is too dear,
with its hopes and invitations,
to waste a moment on
the yesterdays.*
Ralph Waldo Emerson

Don't worry –
If only the people who worry about
their misfortunes, would think about
the riches they have, they would stop
worrying. Would you sell both your
eyes for a million dollars? Or your
hands? Or your hearing? Add up what
you have and you will not sell them
for all the gold in the world. The best
things in life are yours, if you can
appreciate yourself. That's the way to
stop worrying, and start living!
Dale Carnegie

January

LiVE your dream

WEDNESDAY **4**

Stop doing what doesn't work

THURSDAY **5**

Learn from your mistakes

FRIDAY **6**

FULL MOON

Take life one day at a time

SATURDAY **7**

Listen to your heart

SUNDAY **8**

Be pulled by what you love

It's the possibility that keeps me going, not the guarantee.

Albert Camus

MONDAY 9

Good ideas will not work unless you do

TUESDAY 10

Be open to miracles

How far you go in life depends on your being tender with the young, compassionate with the aged, sympathetic with the striving, tolerant of the weak and strong, because someday in your life, you will have been all of these.

George Washington Carver

People will forget what you said; People will forget what you did; But people will never forget how you made them feel.

Maya Angelou

WEDNESDAY 11

Expect the unexpected

January

If you haven't any charity in your heart, you have the worst kind of heart trouble.

Bob Hope

Beauty is simply reality seen with the eyes of love.

Rabindranath Tagore

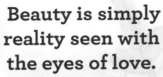

THURSDAY **12**

Every effect has a cause

FRIDAY **13**

In life, stuff happens

SATURDAY **14**

Don't push against the wall, open the door

SUNDAY **15**

Sometimes the end justifies the means

LOOK INSIDE

The creator gathered all of creation and said 'I want to hide something from humans. They are not yet ready for it. It is the realisation that they create their own reality!'

The eagle said 'give it to me, I will take it to the moon'.

The creator said 'no – one day they will go there and find it'.

The salmon said 'I will bury it at the bottom of the ocean'.

The creator said 'no – they will go there too'.

The buffalo said 'I will hide it on the plains'.

The creator said 'no – they will cut the skin of the earth and find it even there'.

Grandmother mole, who lives in the breast of Mother Earth, and one who has no physical eyes, but sees with spiritual vision, said 'put it inside them, they will never look there'.

And the creator said 'it is done'.

Beauty is not in the face; beauty is a light in the heart.

Kahlil Gibran

MONDAY **16**

Every choice has a consequence

TUESDAY **17**

Those who think they know the answer, occasionally do

January

WEDNESDAY **18**

Trust is a rare currency. Value it

THURSDAY **19**

Anyone can be a leader

FRIDAY **20**

Leave others enriched by your interaction

SATURDAY **21**

It's all up to you

SUNDAY **22**

Don't underestimate the power of a kind word

The chief beauty about time
is that you cannot waste it in advance.
The next year, the next day, the next
hour are lying ready for you,
as perfect, as unspoiled,
as if you had never wasted or misapplied
a single moment in all your life.
You can turn over a new leaf every hour
if you choose.

Arnold Bennett

The world is full of magical things,
patiently waiting for our senses
to grow sharper.

WB Yeats

Yesterday is but a dream,
Tomorrow is only a vision.
But today well lived makes every
yesterday a dream of happiness,
and every tomorrow a
vision of hope.

Kālidāsa

**A questioning man is
halfway to being wise.**

Irish proverb

January

MONDAY **23**

You mean the world to someone

TUESDAY **24**

Include everyone

WEDNESDAY **25**

We are each other's destiny

THURSDAY **26**

Dream a new dream

There will always be enough for
everyone's need, but never enough
for everyone's greed.

Mahatma Gandhi

The light heart lives long.

**But I know, somehow,
that only when it is
dark enough can
you see the stars.**

Martin Luther King Jr

*I feel wonderful, because I see,
The love light in your eyes.*

Eric Clapton

*Blessed are the
hearts that can bend;
they shall never
be broken.*

Albert Camus

Let my thoughts come to
you, when I am gone, like the
afterglow of sunset at the
margin of starry silence.

Tagore

January

In all things of nature there is something of the marvellous.

Aristotle

The soul that sees beauty may sometimes walk alone.

Johann Wolfgang von Goethe

FRIDAY 27

Tell great stories that inspire others to achieve great things

SATURDAY 28

Words create worlds

SUNDAY 29

Hope is a radical response to cynicism

MONDAY **30**

Explore new horizons of possibility

TUESDAY **31**

Do not let regrets take the place of your dreams

Nothing is worth more than this day.

Johann Wolfgang von Goethe

We live in the world when we love it.

Tagore

Finish every day and be done with it.
You have done what you could.
Some blunders and absurdities no doubt crept in.
Forget them as soon as you can, tomorrow is a new day;
begin it well and serenely, with too high a spirit
to be encumbered with your old nonsense.

Ralph Waldo Emerson

We shall not cease from exploration,
and the end of all our exploring will
be to arrive where we started and
know the place for the first time.

TS Eliot

If you can dream it,
you can do it.

spriocanna
GOALS
FEABHRA
FEBRUARY

Tús maith leath na hoibre.

A good start is half the work.

Fillean an feall ar
an bhfeallaire.

*The bad deed returns
on the bad deed-doer.*

The eyes do not see what the mind does not want.

Indian wisdom

Progress is impossible without change, and those who cannot change their minds cannot change anything.

George Bernard Shaw

WEDNESDAY 1

Bring all your talents and potential to the table

THURSDAY 2

Everyone is worthy of dignity and respect

FRIDAY 3

Love does not judge

SATURDAY 4

Opportunity can knock very softly

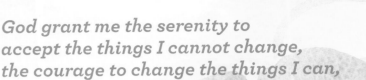

God grant me the serenity to accept the things I cannot change, the courage to change the things I can, and the wisdom to know the difference.

Reinhold Niebuhr

In a gentle way, you can shake the world.

Mahatma Gandhi

The three great mysteries: air to a bird, water to a fish, humankind to itself.

Everything that is made beautiful and fair and lovely is made for the eye of one who sees.

Rumi

SUNDAY **5**

FULL MOON

There is such a thing as an honest mistake

February

> **A warm smile is the universal language of kindness.**
>
> *William Arthur Ward*

NATIVE AMERICAN 10 COMMANDMENTS

Treat the earth and all that dwell therein with respect.
Stay close to the Great Spirit.
Show great respect for your fellow beings.
Work together for the benefit of all mankind.
Give assistance and kindness wherever needed.
Do what you know in your heart to be right.
Look after the wellbeing of mind and body.
Dedicate a share of your efforts to the greater good.
Be truthful and honest at all times.
Take full responsibility for your actions.

> *O, what a tangled web we weave when first we practise to deceive!*
>
> *Walter Scott*

February

*Love's gift cannot
be given, it waits
to be accepted.*

Tagore

MONDAY 6 Bank holiday

Whatever you do, do it well

TUESDAY 7

Kind words can work miracles

WEDNESDAY 8

Smooth seas do not make skilful sailors

THURSDAY 9

Enthusiasm for life shows up in your face

FRIDAY 10

You are unique and valuable

The arts are not a way to make a living. They are a very human way of making life more bearable. Practicing an art, no matter how well or badly, is a way to make your soul grow, for heaven's sake.

Kurt Vonnegut

Today is life — the only life you are sure of. Make the most of today. Get interested in something. Shake yourself awake. Develop a hobby. Let the winds of enthusiasm sweep through you. Live today with gusto.

Dale Carnegie

Only in the agony of parting do we look into the depths of love.

George Eliot

SATURDAY 11

Bad money habits are costly

SUNDAY 12

Do today what you can do today

23

February

**Love all, trust a few,
do wrong to none.**
William Shakespeare

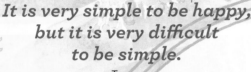

*It is very simple to be happy,
but it is very difficult
to be simple.*
Tagore

MONDAY **13**

Don't indulge in self pity

TUESDAY **14**   St Valentine's Day

We become what we think we are

WEDNESDAY **15**

Forgive everyone for something

THURSDAY **16**

Keep your mind and body active

My dear,
In the midst of hate, I found there was, within me, an invincible love.
In the midst of tears, I found there was, within me, an invincible smile.
In the midst of chaos, I found there was, within me, an invincible calm.
I realised, through it all, that...
In the midst of winter, I found there was, within me, an invincible summer.
And that makes me happy. For it says that no matter how hard the world
pushes against me, within me, there's something stronger –
something better, pushing right back.
Truly yours,
Albert Camus

You want the moon? Just say the word, and I'll throw a lasso around it and pull it down.
It's A Wonderful Life

Maybe it is our imperfections which make us so perfect for one another.
Jane Austen (from Emma)

I guess when you're young you just believe there'll be many people you'll connect with. Later in life you realise it only happens a few times.
Before Sunset (2004)

I long to accomplish a great and noble task, but it is my chief duty to accomplish humble tasks as though they were great and noble. The world is moved along, not only by the mighty shoves of its heroes, but also by the aggregate of the tiny pushes of each honest worker.
Helen Keller

There is no remedy for love but to love more.

Henry David Thoreau

FRIDAY **17**

Surround yourself with beautiful things

SATURDAY **18**

Be positive and encouraging

SUNDAY **19**

Style is never out of fashion

We are not yet what we shall be, but we are growing toward it, the process is not yet finished, but it is going on, this is not the end, but it is the road.

Martin Luther

Oh, I love hugging.
I wish I was an octopus,
so I could hug 10 people
at a time!

Drew Barrymore

February

I like not only to be loved, but also to be told that I am loved.
I am not sure that you are of the same mindut the realm of silence is
large enough beyond the grave. This is the world of light and speech,
and I shall take leave to tell you that you are very dear.

George Eliot

MONDAY **20**

Forgiveness is the key to everything

TUESDAY **21**

There is no such thing as a "little" thing

WEDNESDAY **22**

Even the strongest child needs loving support

THURSDAY **23**

Start to write the story of your life. Begin at the beginning ...

February

FRIDAY **24**

Quiet reflection may help today

SATURDAY **25**

Good enough can be great

SUNDAY **26**

All good things start with a good thought

You become. It takes a long time. That's why it doesn't happen often to people who break easily, or have sharp edges, or who have to be carefully kept. Generally, by the time you are Real, most of your hair has been loved off, and your eyes drop out and you get loose in your joints and very shabby. But these things don't matter at all, because once you are Real you can't be ugly, except to people who don't understand.

The Velveteen Rabbit

MONDAY 27

Schedule personal time into your calendar

TUESDAY 28

Take care of your body

Time is too slow for those who wait,
too swift for those who fear,
too long for those who grieve,
too short for those who rejoice,
but for those who love,
time is eternity.

Henry Van Dyke

A tree is known by its fruit,
a man by his deeds.
A good deed is never lost;
he who sows courtesy
reaps friendship,
and he who plants
kindness gathers love.

Basil St John

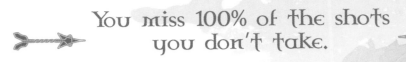

You miss 100% of the shots you don't take.

spriocanna

GOALS

MÁRTA
MARCH

JUST START

An rud is annamh is iontach.
The thing that is seldom is wonderful.

Níl saoi gan locht.
There's not a wise man without fault.

We are all in the gutter, but some of us are looking at the stars.

Oscar Wilde

St Patrick was a gentleman
Who through strategy and stealth
Drove all the snakes from Ireland.
Here's toasting to his health.
But not too many toastings
Lest you lose yourself and then
Forget the good St Patrick
And see all those snakes again.

Henry Bennett

We are beaten, we will make no bones about it; but we are not too badly beaten still to fight.

James Larkin

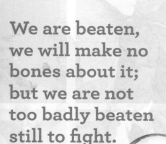

In everyone's life, at some time, our inner fire goes out. It is then burst into flame by an encounter with another human being. We should all be thankful for those people who rekindle the inner spirit.

Albert Schweitzer

WEDNESDAY **1**

A smile can work wonders

THURSDAY **2**

Learn something from the way others do things

March

If you accept your limitations, you go beyond them.

Brendan Behan

Ever tried. Ever failed. No matter. Try Again. Fail again. Fail better.

Samuel Beckett

Be yourself; everyone else is already taken.

Oscar Wilde

Grant me a sense of humour, Lord,
the saving grace to see a joke,
to win some happiness from life,
and pass it on to other folks.

St Thomas More

FRIDAY **3**

Enjoy simple pleasures

SATURDAY **4**

Only you can make the difference here

SUNDAY **5**

Be willing for today to be different

One of the most tragic things I know about human nature is that all of us tend to put off living. We are all dreaming of some magical rose garden over the horizon instead of enjoying the roses that are blooming outside our windows today.

Dale Carnegie

MONDAY 6

When in doubt, muster your courage

Have you ever noticed,
Those people on the wing?
The ones that always pass you by,
And never say a thing.
And even though you know them,
They hurry past in haste,
No quick hello or friendly smile –
They have no time to waste.
For those poor people on the wing,
who never stop to say a thing,
Their minds are full of this and that;
There isn't time to stop and chat.
Until, someday when they're not well,
Will stop you with a tale tell,
Of all the aches and pains they've got –
And off, of course, you too will trot.

Author unknown

TUESDAY 7

FULL MOON

Cherish old friendships

March

WEDNESDAY **8**

Life presents us with opportunities to choose

THURSDAY **9**

Be guided by your principles

FRIDAY **10**

Begin now, where you are

**To learn, one must be humble.
But life is the great teacher.**
James Joyce

Remember my friend, that knowledge is stronger than
memory, and we should not trust the weaker.
Bram Stoker

*Every conquering temptation represents a new fund of
moral energy. Every trial endured and weathered, in the
right spirit, makes a soul nobler and stronger than before.*
William Butler Yeats.

The ordinary acts we practice every day at home are of more importance to the soul than their simplicity might suggest.

Thomas Moore

SATURDAY 11

Rights come with responsibilities

We have no more right to consume happiness without producing it than to consume wealth without producing it.

George Bernard Shaw

Laughter is wine for the soul – laughter soft, or loud and deep, tinged through with seriousness – the hilarious declaration made by man that life is worth living.

Sean O'Casey

Life is like a cup of tea; it's all in how you make it!

Timothy Jeremy

SUNDAY 12

All steps are baby steps

March

MONDAY 13

Be on time

TUESDAY 14

Keep your promises

WEDNESDAY 15

Thoughts are seeds of deeds

THURSDAY 16

Maybe it's not a race to be won

FRIDAY 17 Bank holiday

St Patricks Day

*There are good ships and there are wood ships,
the ships that sail the sea. But the best ships
are friendships, and may they always be.*

Irish proverb

SATURDAY 18

Be who you want to be

SUNDAY 19 Mother's Day

Acknowledge your accomplishments

Mistakes are the portals of discovery.

James Joyce

**Lives of great men all remind us, we can make our lives
sublime, and, departing, leave behind us, footprints on the
sands of time.**

Henry Wadsworth Longfellow

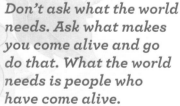

*Don't ask what the world
needs. Ask what makes
you come alive and go
do that. What the world
needs is people who
have come alive.*

Howard Thurman

**You should never be ashamed to admit you have been wrong.
It only proves you are wiser today than yesterday.**

Jonathan Swift

March

May you have the **hindsight** to know where you've been, the **foresight** to know where you're going, and the **insight** to know when you're going too far.

Irish blessing

MONDAY **20**

You act consistent with who you think you are

TUESDAY **21**

You are surrounded by love and beauty

WEDNESDAY **22**

Your life is a mirror of your consistent thoughts

THURSDAY **23**

Rest when you are tired

FRIDAY **24**

You are the most important person in your life

SATURDAY **25**

Learn from how children do things

SUNDAY **26**

Be happy no matter what others say

OLD IRISH PROVERBS

A misty winter brings a pleasant spring,
a pleasant winter a misty spring.
*An old broom knows the dirty corners
best* .
The older the fiddle the sweeter the tune.
A dog owns nothing, yet is seldom
dissatisfied.
What the child sees, the child does.
What the child does, the child is.
The hands are there for friendship,
the heart is there for love.
*The man with the boots does not mind
where he places his foot.*
It's no use giving good advice unless
you have the wisdom to go with it.
It's a good deed to forget a bad joke.

39

> Anyone can sympathise with the sufferings of a friend,
> but it requires a very fine nature to sympathise
> with a friend's success.
>
> *Oscar Wilde*

MONDAY **27**

You get from people what you expect

TUESDAY **28**

Aim for excellence

WEDNESDAY **29**

Your reputation is always left after you

THURSDAY **30**

Miracles happen in moments

FRIDAY **31**

Life is an awesome gift

spriocanna

GOALS

AIBREÁN
APRIL

_____
_____
_____
_____
_____
_____
_____
_____
_____
_____
_____

Is treise an dúchas ná an oillúint.

Nature is stronger than nurture.

Níl aon tintéan mar do thintéan fhéin.

There's no fireplace like your own.

April

A smile

It costs nothing, but creates much. It enriches those who receive, without impoverishing those who give. It happens in a flash and the memory of it sometimes lasts forever. None are so rich they can get along without it and none so poor but are richer for its benefits. It creates happiness in the home, fosters goodwill in a business, and is the countersign of friends. It is rest to the weary, daylight to the discouraged, sunshine to the sad, and nature's best antidote for trouble. Yet it cannot be bought, begged, borrowed or stolen, for it is something that is no earthly good to anyone 'til it is given away. And if in the hurly-burly bustle of today's business world, some of the people you meet should be too tired to give you a smile, may we ask you to leave one of yours? For nobody needs a smile so much as those who have none left to give.

Dale Carnegie

What do we live for, if it is not to make life less difficult for each other?

George Eliot

SATURDAY **1**

Good is a gateway to great

SUNDAY **2**

Actions cause results

When it's better for everyone,
it's better for everyone.

Eleanor Roosevelt

A child, more than all other gifts
that earth can offer to declining man,
brings hope with it, and
forward-looking thoughts.

Wordsworth

MONDAY 3

There is real power in choosing

TUESDAY 4

It doesn't have to be perfect to be wonderful

WEDNESDAY 5

Today is the tomorrow you talked about yesterday

THURSDAY 6

FULL MOON

Believe in yourself

April

It is not a lack of love, but a lack of friendship that makes unhappy marriages.

Friedrich Nietzsche

The opposite of love is not hate, it's indifference.
The opposite of art is not ugliness, it's indifference.
The opposite of faith is not heresy, it's indifference.
And the opposite of life is not death, it's indifference.

Elie Wiesel

FRIDAY 7 Good Friday

Connect with like-minded people

SATURDAY 8

No task is as difficult as your thoughts make it

SUNDAY 9 Easter Sunday

Enjoy the process of living life

When we are no longer able to change a situation, we are challenged to change ourselves.

Viktor Frankl

MONDAY 10 Easter Monday. Bank holiday

Tell your mother you love her

TUESDAY 11

Don't undermine your worth by comparing yourself with others

WEDNESDAY 12

Allow yourself to be powerful

THURSDAY 13

Hurtful words can break hearts

April

Always remember to forget
The things that made you sad.
But never forget to remember
The things that made you glad.

Victor Borge

People are meant to be loved.
Things are meant to be used.
Most of the trouble in the world
comes from things being loved
and people being used.

Dalai Lama

FRIDAY **14**

Take life in bite sized pieces

SATURDAY **15**

You are in the perfect place

SUNDAY **16**

Alone is not a requirement for loneliness

Blessed is the influence of one true, loving
human soul on another.

George Eliot

Do not resent growing old.
Many are denied the privilege.

Mark Twain

We cannot share this sorrow
If we haven't grieved a while.
Nor can we feel another's joy
Until we've learned to smile.

St Patrick

Being deeply loved
by someone gives you
strength, while loving
someone deeply gives
you courage.

Lao Tzu

Simplicity, patience, compassion:
These three are your greatest treasures. **Simple** in actions and thoughts, you return to the source of being. **Patient** with both friends and enemies, you accord with the way things are. **Compassionate** toward yourself, you reconcile all beings in the world.

Lao Tzu

MONDAY **17**

Refuse to indulge in self pity

TUESDAY **18**

Communication makes relationships work

WEDNESDAY **19**

Change happens in baby steps

April

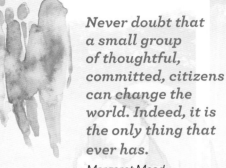

Wisdom is the reward
you get for a lifetime of
listening when you would
rather have talked.

Doug Larson

*Never doubt that
a small group
of thoughtful,
committed, citizens
can change the
world. Indeed, it is
the only thing that
ever has.*

Margaret Mead

THURSDAY **20**

Make new friends

FRIDAY **21**

Live in the moment

SATURDAY **22**

Just show up

SUNDAY **23**

A friend is a gift you give yourself

MONDAY **24**

Do not shy away from risk

TUESDAY **25**

You are not alone

DUST IF YOU MUST

Dust if you must, but wouldn't it be better
To paint a picture, or write a letter,
Bake a cake, or plant a seed;
Ponder the difference between want and need?

Dust if you must, but there's not much time,
With rivers to swim, and mountains to climb;
Music to hear, and books to read;
Friends to cherish, and life to lead.

Dust if you must, but the world's out there
With the sun in your eyes, and the wind in your hair;
A flutter of snow, a shower of rain,
This day will not come around again.

Dust if you must, but bear in mind,
Old age will come and it's not kind.
And when you go (and go you must)
You, yourself, will make more dust.

Rose Milligan

April

WEDNESDAY 26

Keep your dreams alive

THURSDAY 27

Everything in life is temporary

FRIDAY 28

Spend more time with friends

SATURDAY 29

Do not give up while you still have something to give

SUNDAY 30

Where ever you are – be here, now!

SPRIOCANNA
GOALS
BEALTAINE
MAY

_____
_____
_____
_____
_____
_____
_____
_____
_____
_____
_____

*Ní bhíonn an rath
ach mar a mbíonn
an smacht.*

*There is no prosperity
without discipline.*

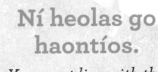

Ní heolas go haontíos.

*You must live with the
person to know them.*

May

GET UP AND GO

How do I know my youth has been spent?
Because my get-up-and-go, got up and went.
But in spite of all that, I'm able to grin,
When I think where my get-up-and-go has been.

When I was young my slippers were red.
I could kick my heels right over my head!
When I grew older my slippers were blue
But I could still dance the whole night through.

Now that I am old my slippers are black
I walk to the corner and puff my way back.
The reason I know my youth is spent
My get-up-and-go got up and went.

Old age is golden, I've heard it said,
And sometimes I wonder as I go to bed.
My ears in a drawer, my teeth in a cup,
My eyes on a table ... will I wake up?

Now I rise in the morning, dust off my wits,
Pick up the paper and read the obits.
If my name is missing, I know I'm not dead.
So I eat a good breakfast and go back to bed.

Anonymous

**Change your thinking, change your thoughts,
change your actions, change your life.**

MONDAY **1** Bank holiday

Never speak badly about yourself

TUESDAY 2

Every good thought is a prayer

> You will be more disappointed in life by the things that you do not do than by the things that you do.
>
> *Mark Twain*

Your life is a mirror of your consistent thoughts.

WEDNESDAY 3

A good example is the best sermon

THURSDAY 4

Growth is evidence of the cycle of life

FRIDAY 5

FULL MOON

Trust your instincts

Open the door to a possible you.
Leave behind the stress and the woe.
Be sure to invite the wonder in,
And let the worries go.

Think of each day as a treasured gift,
And give that gift to yourself.
Accomplish those things that are in your reach,
And leave the rest on the shelf.

Do a world of good in a world that needs,
All the good it can get.
In the course of a day, in every way,
Coming closer to goals and challenges set.

Take or make the time to do,
Those things you've always wanted to.
Choose the path that will gladden your heart,
And live the life that's true to you.

So hold on to your dreams, your hopes to achieve,
All the joys in life you've yet to receive.
Keep the spirit that says "it's only until",
"I Know that I am, I can and I will".

The road ahead may appear uphill ,
And that's the direction your dreams to fulfill.
Anything really is possible to do,
When who you are is true to you.

In the sweetness of friendship let there be laughter,
and sharing of pleasures. For in the dew of little things
the heart finds its morning and is refreshed.

Khalil Gibran

May

Do not take life too seriously; there's none of us getting out alive!

A single conversation across the table with a wise man is better than ten years mere study of books.

Henry Wadsworth Longfellow

One loyal friend is worth ten thousand relatives.

Euripides

Health is the greatest possession. Contentment is the greatest treasure. Confidence is the greatest friend.

Lao Tzu

With the new day comes new strength and new thoughts.

Eleanor Roosevelt

Nobody cares how much you know, until they know how much you care.

Theodore Roosevelt

SATURDAY **6**

If your life feels empty, put more of yourself into it

SUNDAY **7**

Don't spend money you don't have

I am a part of all whom I have met.

Alfred The Great

May

I have never looked upon ease and happiness as ends in themselves. The ideals that have lighted my way, and time after time have given me new courage to face life cheerfully, have been kindness, beauty and truth.

Albert Einstein

MONDAY 8

Silent listening is more healing than words of advice

TUESDAY 9

Be a light in the darkness

WEDNESDAY 10

In trying times don't stop trying

THURSDAY 11

You spread love by giving it wings

Don't limit the child to your own learning;
for they are born for another time.

Rabbinical saying

Let us be grateful to people who make us happy, they are the charming gardeners who make our souls blossom.

Marcel Proust

FRIDAY 12

Worry gives you wrinkles

SATURDAY 13

You can be extraordinary

SUNDAY 14

It's by taking chances that we learn to be brave

The greater danger for most of us lies
not in setting our aim too high and falling short;
but in setting our aim too low, and
achieving our mark.

Michelangelo

May

The only time you should ever look back is to see how far you've come.

Mick Kremling

If you didn't hear it with your own ears or see it with your own eyes, don't invent it with your small mind and share it with your big mouth.

Denise Swanson

We delight in the beauty of the butterfly but rarely admit the changes it has gone through to achieve that beauty.

Maya Angelou

Self confidence is the first prerequisite to great undertakings.

Samuel Johnson

MONDAY **15**

Do it willingly, or not at all

TUESDAY **16**

You attract what you worry about

WEDNESDAY **17**

Harsh words can break spirits

> There are admirable potentialities in every human being. Believe in your strength and your youth. Learn to repeat endlessly to yourself, it all depends on me.
>
> *André Gide*

THURSDAY 18

Laughter is the music of the soul

FRIDAY 19

Master your habits or they will master you

SATURDAY 20

Do something radical

SUNDAY 21

Listen to understand

> *The words that enlighten the soul are more precious than jewels.*
>
> *Hezrat Ina Yat Khan*

> You will begin to heal when you let go of past hurts,
> forgive those who have wronged you and forgive
> yourself for your mistakes.
>
> *Sanvello*

MONDAY **22**

Adversity introduces us to ourselves

TUESDAY **23**

Belief in limits creates limits we believe

WEDNESDAY **24**

Face the reality of the world with courage

For all sad words
of tongue and pen,
the saddest are these
'It might have been'.

John Greenleaf Whittier

Pick battles big enough to matter
and small enough to win.

Jonathan Kozol

May

You can do anything if you have enthusiasm.

Henry Ford

It takes less time to do a thing right, than it does to explain why you did it wrong.

Henry Wadsworth Longfellow

THURSDAY 25

Crown each day with gratitude

FRIDAY 26

Give someone a pleasant surprise

Take time to play –
it is the secret to perpetual youth.
Take time to work –
it is the foundation of success.
Take time to laugh –
it is music for the soul.
Take time to read –
it is access to wisdom.
Take time to be friendly –
it is the road to happiness.
Take time to love –
it is the privilege of life.

Magic time!

May

Life is under no obligation to give us what we expect.

Margaret Mitchell

It's not true that I had nothing on. I had the radio on.

Marilyn Monroe

Anyone can carry their burden, however hard, until nightfall. Anyone can do their work, however hard, for one day. Anyone can live sweetly, patiently, lovingly, purely, till the sun goes down. And this is all life really is.

Robert Louis Stevensen

I shall pass through this life but once. Any good therefore that I can do, let me do it now. Let me not defer or neglect it. For I shall never pass this way again.

Etienne de Grellet

Reject your sense of injury and the injury itself disappears.

Marcus Aurelius

SATURDAY **27**

Remember where you came from – and it's not where you're going

---

SUNDAY **28**

Don't complicate your life

MONDAY 29

Take a break

TUESDAY 30

Be an encourager

Being Irish, he had an abiding sense of tragedy, which sustained him through temporary periods of joy.

William Butler Yeats

Understand yourself better so you can better understand others.

Demand not that events should happen as you wish; but wish them to happen as they do happen, and your life will be serene.

Epictetus

I complained that I had no shoes, until I saw a man who had no feet.

Confucius

WEDNESDAY 31

'One day' is far away

The secret of getting ahead is getting started.

spriocanna

GOALS

MEITHEAMH
JUNE

Ní neart go cur le chéile.

There is strength when we pull together.

An té a bhíonn siúlach, bíonn scéalach.

He who travels has stories to tell.

> If I have seen further than others, it is by standing upon the shoulders of giants.
>
> *Isaac Newton*

> As we express our gratitude, we must never forget that the highest appreciation is not to utter words, but to live by them.
>
> *John F Kennedy*

> Do not wait: the time will never be 'just right'. Start where you stand, and work whatever tools you may have at your command and better tools will be found as you go along.
>
> *Napoleon Hill*

> *The cave you fear to enter holds the treasure you seek. Fear of the unknown is our greatest fear. While caution is a useful instinct, we lose many opportunities and much of the adventure of life if we fail to support the curious explorer within us.*
>
> *Joseph Campbell*

THURSDAY **1**

Anything is possible

June

If you can dream it, you can do it.

Walt Disney

I think one's feelings waste themselves in words, they ought all to be distilled into actions and into actions which bring results.

Florence Nightingale

A CREED TO HEED

1   Prayer is not just a spare wheel that you pull out when in trouble, but can be a steering wheel that directs the right path throughout the journey.

2   A car's windshield is large while the rear view mirror is small. Our past is not as important as our future. So, keep your eyes on the road ahead. Make a turn when necessary.

3   Friendship is like a book. It takes years to write, yet a few minutes to burn.

4   All things in life are temporary. If going well, enjoy it, it will not last forever. If going badly, don't worry, that won't last long either.

5   Old friends are like gold! New friends are like diamonds! If you find a diamond, don't throw out the gold! In a precious ring, the diamond is neatly held in a base of gold.

6   Often when we lose hope and think this is the end of the road, look up. God smiles from above to show us it's merely a bend in the road.

7   When God solves your problems, you have faith in His abilities. When God doesn't solve your problems, He has faith in yours.

8   A blind person asked St Anthony: Can there be anything worse than losing your sight?" He replied: Yes, losing your vision!"

9   Worrying does not take away tomorrow's troubles, it takes away today's peace.

10 When you pray for others, God listens to your prayers, and sometimes, when you are feeling blessed, consider someone, somewhere has prayed for you.

> **I am not what happened to me,**
> **I am what I choose to become.**
>
> *Carl Jung*

FRIDAY **2**

Turn your dreams into goals

SATURDAY **3**

Play fair

SUNDAY **4**

FULL MOON

Reach out to others – take the first step

> **The greatest deception men suffer is from their own opinions.**
>
> *Leonardo da Vinci*

> **What lies behind us and what lies before us are tiny matters compared to what lies within us.**
>
> *Ralph Waldo Emerson*

> *If we couldn't laugh, we would all go insane.*
>
> *Jimmy Buffett*

June

Whatever the mind can conceive and believe, it can achieve.

Napoleon Hill

MONDAY 5 Bank holiday

Happiness is 'in here' not 'out there'

TUESDAY 6

Choices come at us, one at a time

WEDNESDAY 7

Obstacles strengthen us

THURSDAY 8

See the good in others

FRIDAY 9

Self-discovery is a life-long process

> And one has to understand that braveness is not the absence of fear but rather the strength to keep on going forward despite the fear.
>
> *Paulo Coelho*

SATURDAY **10**

This too will pass

SUNDAY **11**

What comes out of your mouth designs your life

Life shrinks or expands in proportion to one's courage.

Anais Nin

Energy and persistence conquer all things.

Benjamin Franklin

Don't say you don't have enough time or enough money to change the world. You have exactly the same number of hours per day that were given to Helen Keller, Gandhi, Michelangelo, Mother Teresa, Leonardo da Vinci and Jesus Christ.

Shannon L Alder

People do not like to think. If one thinks, one must reach conclusions. Conclusions are not always pleasant.

Helen Keller

June

MONDAY **12**

Forgiveness heals a broken heart

TUESDAY **13**

The most important moment of your life is this one

WEDNESDAY **14**

Change can be joyful if you embrace it willingly

THURSDAY **15**

A life lived in fear is a life half-lived

FRIDAY **16**

Be ready to lend a helping hand

It will never rain roses: when we want to have more roses, we must plant more roses.

George Eliot

SATURDAY 17

Laughter lightens the load

SUNDAY 18 Father's Day

Honesty is the best policy

Human wisdom says don't put off until tomorrow what can be done today. But I tell you, that those who know how to put off until tomorrow are most agreeable to God. They who sleep like a child are also they who sleep like my darling Hope. So, I tell you, put off until tomorrow those worries and those troubles which are gnawing at you today, and might very well devour you today. Put off until tomorrow those sobs that choke you when you see today's unhappiness, those sobs that rise up and strangle you. Put off until tomorrow those tears that fill your eyes and your head, flooding you, rolling down your cheeks. Because, between now and tomorrow, maybe God will have passed your way. Blessed are those who put it off, that is to say, blessed are they who hope and who sleep.

Charles Péguy

> The righteous person acts out of pity,
> yet leaves many things undone.
> The moral person will act out of duty,
> and, when no one will respond,
> will roll up their sleeves and use force.
> The kind person acts from the heart, and
> accomplishes a multitude of things.
>
> *Lao Tzu*

MONDAY **19**

You are more capable than you know

TUESDAY **20**

Look, listen, choose, act

WEDNESDAY **21**

Nothing lasts forever

THURSDAY **22**

Appreciate your home and your family

June

There is more to life than simply increasing its speed.

Mahatma Gandhi

Friendship improves happiness and abates misery, by the doubling of our joy and the dividing of our grief.

Cicero

Rest is not idleness, and to lie sometimes on the grass under trees on a summer's day, listening to the murmur of the water, or watching the clouds float across the sky, is by no means a waste of time.

John Lubbock

FRIDAY 23

Never run yourself down

SATURDAY 24

There are no stupid questions

SUNDAY 25

Listen before you speak

MONDAY **26**

Keep your promises

TUESDAY **27**

Well begun is half done

WEDNESDAY **28**

Eat less junk food

THURSDAY **29**

Nobody is perfect

FRIDAY **30**

It's fun to learn new things

Sticks in a bundle are unbreakable.

Kenyan proverb

Luck is preparedness meeting opportunity.

spriocanna

GOALS

IÚIL
JULY

_____
_____
_____
_____
_____
_____
_____
_____
_____
_____
_____
_____

Níor bhris focal maith fiacail riamh.

A good word never broke a tooth.

July

If it were not for **hope** the heart would break.

Thomas Fuller

We could never have loved the earth so well if we had had no childhood in it, if it were not the earth where the same flowers come up again every spring, that we used to gather with our tiny fingers, as we sat lisping to ourselves on the grass; the same hips and haws on the autumn hedgerows; the same redbreasts that we used to call 'God's birds' because they did no harm to the precious crops. What novelty is worth that sweet monotony where everything is known and loved because it is known?

George Eliot

Across the fields of yesterday
he sometimes comes to me.
A little lad just back from play
– the lad I used to be.
And yet he smiles so wistfully,
when he has crept within,
I wonder if he hopes to see
the man I might have been.

Robert F Jones

SATURDAY **1**

Be your own best friend

SUNDAY **2**

Kindness begins at home

The difficulty lies not so much in developing new ideas as in escaping from old ones.

John Maynard Keynes

MONDAY **3**

FULL MOON

Most of what you worry about never happens

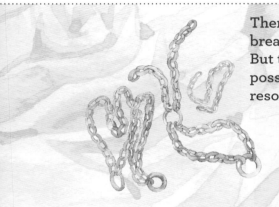

There are truly no chains so hard to break than those of our own forging. But they are not hopeless. The worst possible habits will yield to human resolution and strength from above.

D Williamson

TUESDAY **4**

Get enough sleep

WEDNESDAY **5**

All you give is given to yourself

July

Optimism is the faith that leads to achievement, but nothing can be done without hope.

Helen Keller

Happiness is like a kiss. You must share it to enjoy it.

Bernard Meltzer

THURSDAY 6

Be a shining example

FRIDAY 7

Be willing to ask for what you want — you might get it

SATURDAY 8

Miracles can happen

SUNDAY 9

Stumbling is not falling

There's something that pulls us up
And something that drags us down;
And the consequence is we wobble
Twixt muck and a golden crown.

Anon

Fear knocked at the door.
Faith answered. No one was there.

MONDAY **10**

O ... is for opportunity

TUESDAY **11**

Every storm is followed by a rainbow

WEDNESDAY **12**

Life is worth living

THURSDAY **13**

There are many goals in a long game

July

It is moments like these that force us to try harder, dig deeper, and discover gifts we never knew we had; to find the greatness that lies within each of us.

Barak Obama

FRIDAY 14

You will be as successful as you make up your mind to be

SATURDAY 15

Make friends with interesting people

SUNDAY 16

It's ok to make mistakes

EIGHT STEPS TO HAPPINESS
Think less – ponder more.
Frown less – smile more.
Know less – wonder more.
Argue less – listen more.
Judge less – accept more.
Observe less – participate more.
Complain less – appreciate more.
Fear less – encourage more.

To make no mistakes is not in the power of man; but from their errors and mistakes the wise and good learn wisdom for the future.

Plutarch

The woods are lovely, dark and deep.
But I have promises to keep,
And miles to go before I sleep.

Robert Frost

I slept and dreamt that life
was joy. I awoke and saw that
life was service. I acted and
behold, service was joy.

Tagore

MONDAY **17**

Make that call

Three sisters age 92, 94 and 96 live in a house together. One
night the 96 year old draws a bath, puts her foot in and pauses.
She yells down the stairs, Was I getting in or out of the bath?"
The 94 year old yells back, I don't know, I'll come up and see.
She starts up the stairs and pauses, then she yells,
Was I going up the stairs or coming down?"
The 92 year old was sitting at the kitchen
table having tea listening to her sisters.
She shakes her head and says, I sure hope
I never get that forgetful. She knocks
on wood for good measure. She then yells,
I'll come up and help both of you as soon
as I see who's at the door.

TUESDAY **18**

Put into it what you want to get out of it

July

Dream no small dreams for they have no power to move the hearts of men.

Goethe

WEDNESDAY 19

Your creativity is always in demand

THURSDAY 20

Be a conscious contribution

FRIDAY 21

Perfection is a word in the dictionary

SATURDAY 22

It's never crowded along the extra mile

SUNDAY 23

You attract what you put your attention on

Through our great good fortune, in our youth our hearts are touched with fire. It is given to us to learn at the outset that life is a profound and passionate thing.

Oliver Wendell Homes

MONDAY 24

Little things can make a big difference

TUESDAY 25

Reconnect with an old friend

WEDNESDAY 26

Be kind to the earth — reduce, reuse, restore, recycle

Faith is the bird that feels the light and sings when the dawn is still dark.

Rabindranath Tagore

In a world filled with hate, we must still dare to hope.
In a world filled with anger, we must still dare to comfort.
In a world filled with despair, we must still dare to dream.
And in a world filled with distrust, we must still dare to believe.

Michael J

**Blessed are they who expect nothing,
for they shall never be disappointed.**

Alexander Pope

**It is greed to do all the talking but
not to want to listen at all.**

Democritus

**Hope itself is like a star
– not to be seen in the
sunshine of prosperity,
and only to be discovered
in the night of adversity.**

CH Spurgeon

*There is no doubt that creativity is the most
important human resource of all. Without creativity
there would be no progress and we would forever be
repeating the same patterns.*

Edward de Bono

Sickness is a hindrance to the body,
but not to your ability to choose,
unless that is your choice. Lameness
is a hindrance to the leg, but not to
your ability to choose. Say this to
yourself with regard to everything
that happens, then you will see such
obstacles as hindrances to something
else, but not to yourself.

Epictetus

**They who dream for too
long will become like
their shadow.**

Indian proverb

July

Nobody can hurt me without
my permission.
Mahatma Gandhi

THURSDAY 27

Ponder over some exciting goals

FRIDAY 28

To get there, you have to start here

Gratitude can transform common days into
thanksgivings, turn routine jobs into joy, and
change ordinary opportunities into blessings.
Feeling gratitude and not expressing it is like
wrapping a present and not giving it.
William Arthur Ward

SATURDAY 29

It's easier said than done

SUNDAY 30

Bring the best you have

Over every mountain there is a path, although it may not be seen from the valley.

Theodore Roethke

Our greatest weakness lies in giving up. The most certain way to succeed is always to try just one more time.

Thomas Edison

It is better to keep your mouth closed and let people think you are a fool than to open it and remove all doubt.

Mark Twain

Never impose on another what you would not choose for yourself.

Confucius

You sometimes forget the harm that was done to you, but never the harm you have done to others.

Eastern wisdom

MONDAY **31**

Forgive your family

A stumbling block to the pessimist is
a stepping stone to the optimist.

spriocanna
GOALS
LÚNASA
AUGUST

_____

_____

_____

_____

_____

*Is fearr an
tsláinte ná
na táinte.*

_____

_____

**Health is
preferable
to wealth.**

_____

_____

_____

Is minic a bhris béal
duine a shrón.

*Many a time a man's mouth
broke his nose.*

August

No one is so brave they are not disturbed by something unexpected.

Julius Caesar

TUESDAY 1

FULL MOON

Listen to your own speaking

WEDNESDAY 2

Get excited by a new adventure

You must understand the whole of life, not just one little part of it. That is why you must read, that is why you must look at the skies, that is why you must sing and dance, and write poems and suffer and understand, for all of that is life.

Jiddu Krishnamurthy

In the depth of winter I finally learned that there was in me an invincible summer.

Albert Camus

As we express our gratitude, we must never forget that the highest appreciation is not to utter words, but to live by them.

John F Kennedy

Every man has his secret sorrows which the world knows not; and often times we call a man cold when he is only sad.

Henry Wadsworth Longfellow

15 WAYS TO LOVING YOUR LIFE

Discover who you are. Think about what makes you, you, and just like a beautiful flower that needs watering to blossom, learn to appreciate yourself and nurture your most lovable qualities.

Eliminate self criticism. Avoid the temptation to listen to that little internal voice that berates you over the tiniest thing. It's not true that you are "no good" or "useless" or "stupid" simply because you made a mistake. Don't pay attention to that voice.

Be kind and positive. When you start to think kindly and positively of yourself the acceptance and love you have for yourself and your life grows.

Acknowledge your accomplishments. It's not always about working towards future achievements, it's those small lovely wins that show you how it's done.

Let go of worry. Worry gives you wrinkles! Loving yourself requires that you let go of what others think about you. Let them worry!

Be truthful to yourself and your life. Loving your life requires you to be truthful about your own feelings. Love honesty. Who loves a liar!

Grow spiritually. When you spend time growing spiritually, you become peaceful, connected, loving, kind and compassionate.

Make positive affirmations every day. Declaring positive affirmations affirms all that is positive about your life and who you can be, and will help raise your self-esteem every day. Put them where you can read them and read them with conviction!

Express gratitude – for the life you have, and the person you are becoming. Express appreciation for your strengths and gifts and the opportunity to be you.

Nurture your dreams. When you nurture your dreams you can also love the life you are already living, knowing your dreams are on their way.

Boost your self-confidence. Take every opportunity that can develop your sense of what you can do. Every step counts.

Relax. You need to give yourself time and space to be at peace with the world. Step back occasionally and watch. Listen. Breathe.

Have fun. Smile. Laugh. Do stuff purely for the fun of it. Life is meant to be enjoyed. That's what friendships are for.

Look after your body. It's important to nourish and strengthen your body and mind with proper nutrition and regular exercise.

Learn to see beauty. When you notice the beauty in everything you see around you, you will also see beauty in yourself. Stop and smell the roses. See everything.

Notice everything. Feel everything. Love everything. Everything is beautiful in its own way. When you see the world this way, you will truly love life, and life becomes a real joy.

August

Dear Self

I am working on being a better person.
Please ...
Let me be the type of person I would admire if I saw them in action.
Let me greet each day as another opportunity to get it right.
Let me be open to thinking about things in a way
I haven't thought about them before.
Let me not shy away from trying new things just
because I'm afraid of failing or looking foolish.
Let me face my fears and do the things I would
like to do, even when they make me nervous.
Let me be generous with what I have to give, and
be confident enough to encourage others.
Let me remember to be thankful for what I have, and the choices in my life.
Let me accept my mistakes as valuable learning experiences.
Let me not be so worried about what other people think.
Let me learn to love myself, flaws and all.
Let me be patient as I discover what I want
to do, and who I want to be, in my life.
Let me be proud of who I am, and who I am becoming.
Best wishes.
Me

There is a loneliness in this world so great, you can see it in the slow movement of a clock's hands.

Charles Bukowski

THURSDAY 3

Exercise your influence with calm

When dealing with people, remember you are not dealing with creatures of logic, but creatures of emotion.

Dale Carnegie

The greatest deception men suffer is from their own opinions.

Leonardo da Vinci

FRIDAY **4**

Real power does not require open display

SATURDAY **5**

There is always a higher purpose

To conquer loneliness, you must leave the shadows of self pity, and walk into the bright light of adventure, meeting new people and making new friends. Walk gaily into places where you can share what you have to offer, your smile, your happiness, your life, your dreams. Be confident. You have everything you need.

**Don't cry because it's over.
Smile because it happened.**

Dr Seuss

SUNDAY **6**

Invite a friend over for dinner

August

Most of us have far more courage than we ever dreamed we possessed.

Dale Carnegie

What if you could know the unknowable, change the unchangeable, accept the unacceptable, forgive the unforgiveable and believe the unbelievable? Could the impossible become possible?

MONDAY 7 Bank holiday

Your actions are always under your control

TUESDAY 8

Travel new paths to reach new destinations

WEDNESDAY 9

Excellence is a matter of attitude

THURSDAY 10

Everything exists in language

The strongest of all warriors are these two – time and patience.

Leo Tolstoy

FRIDAY **11**

Plan a romantic dinner date

SATURDAY **12**

You can't master what you are unaware of

Perhaps the mission of an artist is to interpret beauty to people – the beauty within themselves.

Langston Hughes

They say I'm old-fashioned, and live in the past, but sometimes I think progress progresses too fast!

Dr Seuss

You will never find time for anything. If you want time, you must make it.

Charles Buxton

SUNDAY **13**

Choose the sensible approach

August

Why is it that when someone tells you there are a billion stars in the sky, you believe them but if they tell you a wall has wet paint, you have to touch it to be sure?

MONDAY **14**

New experiences can seem scary

TUESDAY **15**

Start as you mean to go on

WEDNESDAY **16**

Remember what got you here

I found love when I was with myself. I went with nature, with animals, and I found love and harmony. I would come home at the end of the day – braids pulled out, my dress torn – and of course I got asked, "Where have you been all day!?" But I had been in a world of love and happiness.

Tina Turner

THURSDAY 17

Listen to the end ... and beyond

The way to get started is to quit talking and begin doing.

Walt Disney

Don't set a goal to achieve a goal. Set a goal so you can become the person you need to be to achieve that goal.

Ralph Waldo Emerson

In order to cause a shadow to disappear, you must shine a light on it.

Shakti Gawain

FRIDAY 18

Have a bath by candlelight

SATURDAY 19

Strengthen your resolve

SUNDAY 20

Ask better questions

Be careful what you water your dreams with.
Water them with worry and fear and you will produce weeds
that choke the life from your dream. Water them with optimism
and solutions and you will cultivate success. Always be on the
lookout for ways to turn a problem into an opportunity for success.
Always be on the lookout for ways to nurture your dream.

Lao Tzu

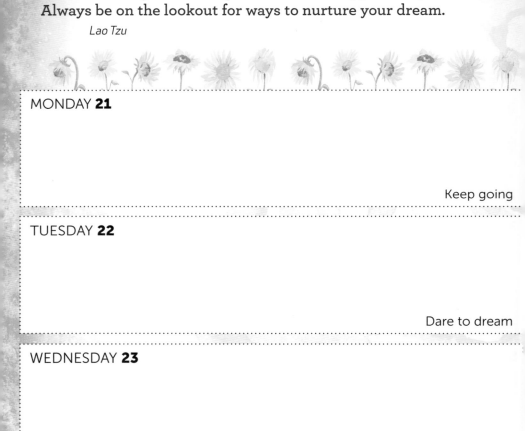

MONDAY **21**

Keep going

TUESDAY **22**

Dare to dream

WEDNESDAY **23**

Stand firm for what is right

THURSDAY **24**

Place yourself high on your priority list

August

Life shrinks or expands in proportion to one's courage.
Anais Nin

Some people care too much. I think it's called love.
Winnie the Pooh

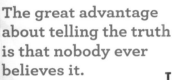

The great advantage about telling the truth is that nobody ever believes it.
Dorothy L Sayers

I am not what happened to me, I am what I choose to become.
Carl Jung

FRIDAY 25

Visualise the ideal outcome

SATURDAY 26

Allow others to contribute

SUNDAY 27

It gets easier

August

dreams come true

MONDAY 28

Often, silence is the best answer

TUESDAY 29

Life always gives you another chance

WEDNESDAY 30

Watch a feel good movie

Real generosity toward the future lies in giving all to the present.

Albert Camus

THURSDAY 31

FULL MOON

You life is filled with wonderful people

*Once you choose hope,
anything is possible.*

SPRIOCANNA

GOALS

MEÁN FOMHAIR
SEPTEMBER

*Nuair a
bhíonn an
fíon istigh,
bíonn
an ciall
amuigh.*

*When the
wine is in,
sense is out.*

**Aithníonn ciaróg
ciaróg eile.**

It takes one to know one.

September

Believe that life is worth living and your belief will help create the fact.

William James

The infinite wonders of the universe are revealed to us in exact measure as we are capable of receiving them. The keenness of our vision depends not on how much we can see, but on how much we feel.

Helen Keller

FRIDAY 1

Understand yourself better to better understand others

SATURDAY 2

Be generous with your time

SUNDAY 3

Strive for excellence, not perfection

Grown-ups never understand anything by themselves, and it is tiresome for children to be always and forever explaining things to them.

Antoine de Saint-Exupéry

The most common way people give up their power is by thinking they don't have any.

Alice Walker

I judge you unfortunate because you have never lived through misfortune. You have passed through life without an opponent — no one can ever know what you are capable of, not even you.

Seneca

It is during our darkest moments that we must focus to see the light.

Aristotle

He who has let go of hatred, who treats all beings with kindness and compassion, who is always serene, unmoved by pain or pleasure, free of the "I" and "mine," self-controlled, firm and patient, his whole mind focused on me — that is the person I love best.

The Bhagavad Gita

The key is to keep company only with people who uplift you, whose presence calls forth your best.

Epictetus

When we strive to become better than we are, everything around us becomes better too.

Paulo Coelho

September

MONDAY **4**

Leave everything a little better than you found it

TUESDAY **5**

Focus on making things better, not bigger

WEDNESDAY **6**

Don't cut what can be untied

THURSDAY **7**

Always leave yourself room to manoeuvre

FRIDAY **8**

Give someone one of your smiles

Knowing yourself is the beginning of all wisdom.

Aristotle

Every battle is won before it is fought.

Sun Tzu

If we had a keen vision and feeling of all ordinary human life, it would be like hearing the grass grow and the squirrel's heart beat, and we should die of that roar which lies on the other side of silence.

George Eliot

Love is the basis of who you are. Anything other than love as an expression of your being, is artificial and unnatural, and is a result of not knowing who you are.

SATURDAY **9**

Browse in a bookshop

SUNDAY **10**

Surprise a friend

September

MONDAY 11

Be good to your neighbours

TUESDAY 12

Do something out of the ordinary

Fall in love with what you do; trust in what you're doing; believe in what you're doing and what you do will be wonderful.

It's not until something is broken that we realise it was breakable.

WEDNESDAY 13

Start writing the story of your life

There is no great genius without a mixture of madness.

Aristotle

If you have built castles in the air, your work need not be lost; that is where they should be. Now put the foundations under them.

Henry David Thoreau

THURSDAY **14**

Who said life was fair?

FRIDAY **15**

Make peace with your past to liberate your future

SATURDAY **16**

Give time, time

SUNDAY **17**

Life is a school and we are here to learn

September

The very essence of romance is uncertainty.

Oscar Wilde

MONDAY **18**

Reach out to others

TUESDAY **19**

The only person you can change is yourself

WEDNESDAY **20**

One good laugh a day is essential medicine

Those who trust us, educate us.

George Eliot

Educating the mind without educating the heart is no education at all.

Aristotle

Love never dies a natural death. It dies because we don't know how to replenish its source. It dies of blindness and errors and betrayals. It dies of illness and wounds; it dies of weariness, of witherings, of tarnishings.

Anais Nin

Animals are such agreeable friends. They ask no questions, they pass no criticisms.

George Eliot

This above all: to thine own self be true,
And it must follow, as the night the day,
Thou canst not then be false to any man.

William Shakespeare

THURSDAY 21

Let love in, let hurt out

FRIDAY 22

In every conflict there is growth

SATURDAY 23

Watch your moods – they can wreak havoc

SUNDAY 24

Give up the need to control

September

> We have to dare to be ourselves, however frightening or strange that self may prove to be.
>
> *May Sarton*

MONDAY 25

You are not alone

TUESDAY 26

Be a good friend

WEDNESDAY 27

Enjoy the great outdoors

THURSDAY 28

Don't curse the dark — light a candle

You do not write your life with words.
You write it with actions. What you think is not
important. It is only important what you do.

Patrick Ness

Without music, life would be a mistake.

Friedrich Nietzsche

*It's easier to fool people
than convince them they
have been fooled.*

Mark Twain

Do not fear to be eccentric in opinion,
for every opinion now accepted,
was once eccentric.

Bertrand Russell

FRIDAY **29**

FULL MOON

Clear out the clutter

SATURDAY **30**

In a moment of doubt, trust yourself

Only those who dare to fail greatly
can ever achieve greatly.

spriocanna

GOALS

DEIREADH
FOMHAIR
OCTOBER

---

*Mol an óige agus
tiocfaidh si.*

Praise the young and they
will come on.

12 THINGS WORTH REMEMBERING

The past cannot be changed but your view of the past can.
Opinions don't define your reality, they express someone else's.
Everyone's journey is different, concentrate on your own.
Many things get better with time, and some get worse.
Judgements are a confession of character.
Overthinking will lead to anxiety.
Happiness is found within when you serve without.
Positive thoughts lead to positive actions.
Smiles are contagious.
Kindness is free.
You only fail if you quit.
What goes around comes around.

LOVE AFTER LOVE

*The time will come when, with elation, you will greet
yourself arriving at your own door, in your own mirror,
and each will smile at the other's welcome, and say, sit
here. Eat. You will love again the stranger who
was your self. Give wine. Give bread. Give back
your heart to itself, to the stranger who has loved
you all your life, whom you ignored for another,
who knows you by heart. Take down the love letters
from the bookshelf, the photographs, the desperate
notes, peel your own image from the mirror.
Sit. Feast on your life.*

Derek Walcott

**Action may not always bring happiness;
but there is no happiness without action.**

Benjamin Disraeli

SUNDAY **1**

Don't let others define you

October

MONDAY 2

Go with the flow of life

Kind words can be short and easy to speak, but their echoes are truly endless.

Mother Theresa

No idea is so outlandish that it should not be considered with a searching, but at the same time a steady eye.

Winston Churchill

TUESDAY 3

Make an appointment for a medical check up

WEDNESDAY 4

A heart in love with life never grows old

THURSDAY 5

Anger is one letter short of danger

Most people don't aim too high for fear they'll miss, so they aim too low and are perhaps disappointed when they hit.

FRIDAY **6**

Remind yourself "I've come a long way"

SATURDAY **7**

Don't just be a doer, be a doer of good deeds

SUNDAY **8**

Fill your life with what you love

Daring ideas are like chessmen moved forward: they may be beaten, but they may start a winning game.

Johann Wolfgang von Goethe

October

MONDAY 9

Stay optimistic and confident

TUESDAY 10

A little kindness goes a long way

WEDNESDAY 11

Don't be one of life's begrudgers

You were born to win, but to be a winner, you must plan to win, prepare to win, and expect to win.
Zig Ziglar

The only true forgiveness is that which is offered and extended even before the offended has apologised and sought it.
Sören Kirkegard

There is as much greatness of mind in acknowledging a good turn as in doing it.
Seneca

Accomplish the great tasks by a series of small acts.

Tao Te Ching

THURSDAY 12

Listen to learn something new today

FRIDAY 13

Time you enjoy wasting, is not wasted time

SATURDAY 14

Don't give up on yourself

SUNDAY 15

Life would be dull without human error

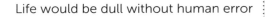

A pile of rocks ceases to be a rock when somebody contemplates it with the idea of a cathedral in mind.

Antoine de St-Exupery

Happiness is not something ready-made. It comes from your own actions.

Dalai Lama

October

Ideas come from everything.

Alfred Hitchcock

MONDAY **16**

There is an artist in everybody

TUESDAY **17**

Keep a cool head – and a warm heart

WEDNESDAY **18**

Happiness is not a destination to arrive at

THURSDAY **19**

Whatever happens, you will handle it

FRIDAY **20**

Trust all is working out perfectly

As soon as you trust yourself, you will know how to live.

Johann Wolfgang von Goethe

When nobody else celebrates you, then celebrate yourself. When nobody else compliments you, then compliment yourself. It's not other peoples' job to make you happy. It's up to you. Happiness is an inside job.

Joel Osteen

SATURDAY **21**

Consider the alternatives

SUNDAY **22**

Be your own best company

To succeed in life you need three things: A wishbone, a backbone and a funnybone.

Reba McEntyre

Painting is silent poetry, and poetry is painting that speaks.

Plutarch

Clouds come floating into my life, no longer to carry rain or usher storm, but to add colour to my sunset sky.

Rabindranath Tagore

October

Love and desire are the spirit's wings to great deeds.
Johann Wolfgang von Goethe

MONDAY 23

Be optimistic about your future

TUESDAY 24

Focus on the gifts you have received

WEDNESDAY 25

It's always the right time to express gratitude

THURSDAY 26

Improvement begins with "I"

Never regret anything that has happened in your life – it cannot be changed, undone or forgotten. It can be forgiven. It can be taken as a lesson learned. Leave it be and move on.

Author unknown

*The path to success is never a straight line.
It's the seeds that we sow by our failures that
determine our ultimate results.*

**Do not judge
my story by the
chapter you
walked in on.**

Mark Twain

**Hide our
ignorance as we
will, an evening
of wine soon
reveals it.**

Heraclitus

FRIDAY 27

We are all more or less able and capable than we think

SATURDAY 28

FULL MOON

Be kind to the earth

SUNDAY 29

Overlove yourself

**Tis better to have loved and lost
than never to have loved at all.**

Alfred Lord Tennyson

*Two monologues do not
a dialogue make.*

October

MONDAY **30** Bank holiday

Do not be ashamed to cry

TUESDAY **31**

There is only now and it's happening now

HEAVEN ON EARTH

Live with kindness and integrity.
Conduct yourself with grace under pressure.
Be an asset in the lives of others.
Put people before things and live from your heart.
Be intelligent, but know it is better to be kind than smart.
Be a peacemaker who values peace and takes peace everywhere you go.
Have among your priorities the characteristics of politeness,
compassion and patience.
Avoid making rash assumptions.
Be a believer in true love.
Be truthful and honest in your dealings.
Communicate clearly and simply and without sarcasm.
Know that anger is one letter short of danger.
Laugh and make the best of every situation.
Understand that life is not perfect.
Understand you are enough.
Learn to love and to be loved.
Home is where your heart is.
When you come home to yourself you will find heaven on Earth.

The only way to do great work is to love what you do.

spriocanna
GOALS
SAMHAIN
NOVEMBER

_____
_____
_____
_____
_____
_____
_____
_____
_____

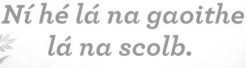

Ní hé lá na gaoithe lá na scolb.

A windy day is not a day for thatching.

November

When I was young, I wanted to change the world.
I found it difficult to change the world, so I tried to change my nation. When I found I couldn't change my nation, I began to focus on my town. I couldn't change my town.
When I got older, I tried to change my family ...
Now I am old, I realise the only thing I can change is myself.
I realise, that if, long ago, I had changed myself, I could have made an impact on my family. My family and I could have made an impact on our town.
Our impact could have changed our nation and I could indeed have changed the world!

Unknown Monk 1100 AD

A loving heart is the truest wisdom.

Charles Dickens

Nothing is impossible, the word itself says 'I'm possible'!

Audrey Hepburn

WEDNESDAY 1

Your life can be what you want it to be

THURSDAY 2

What are you bringing to the table?

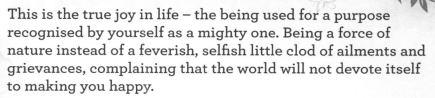

This is the true joy in life – the being used for a purpose recognised by yourself as a mighty one. Being a force of nature instead of a feverish, selfish little clod of ailments and grievances, complaining that the world will not devote itself to making you happy.

I am of the opinion that my life belongs to the community and as long as I live it is my privilege to do for it whatever I can. I want to be thoroughly used up when I die, for the harder I work the more I live. I rejoice in life for its own sake.

Life is no brief candle to me. It's a sort of splendid torch I have got hold of for the moment, and I want to make it burn as brightly as possible before handing it over to future generations.

George Bernard Shaw

FRIDAY 3

It's never too late to change your mind

SATURDAY 4

Permission granted

SUNDAY 5

You become what you say you are

November

Keep your face always toward the sunshine and shadows will fall behind you.

Walt Whitman

MONDAY 6

We all make our share of honest mistakes

TUESDAY 7

To those who search, life reveals its mystery

WEDNESDAY 8

When looking for answers, look within

THURSDAY 9

Speak with intention

Never give up on a dream just because of the time it will take to accomplish it. The time will pass anyway.

Earl Nightingale

Comparison is the thief of joy.
Theodore Roosevelt

FRIDAY 10

Fuel your actions with purpose

One word frees us of all the weight and pain of life: that word is love.
Sophocles

A flower does not think of competing with the flower next to it. It just blooms where it's planted.

The future belongs to those who believe in the beauty of their dreams.
Eleanor Roosevelt

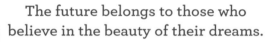

SATURDAY 11

Nothing wastes more time than worrying

SUNDAY 12

Light a candle for a special intention

November

Dead people receive more flowers than the living ones because regret is stronger than gratitude.
Anne Frank

If you realised how powerful your thoughts are, you would never think a negative thought.
Peace Pilgrim

MONDAY **13**

All you give is given to yourself

TUESDAY **14**

Don't put limits on yourself

WEDNESDAY **15**

Explore new possibilities

This is the real secret of life — to be completely engaged with what you are doing in the here and now. And instead of calling it work, realise it is play.
Alan Watts

A life lived without forgiveness is a prison.

William Arthur Ward

THURSDAY 16

We don't know the half of it

FRIDAY 17

Everything is possible

SATURDAY 18

Talk is never cheap

SUNDAY 19

It's ok to say 'yes' or 'no'

The world will persist in exhibiting before you what you persist in affirming to the world.

Emma Curtis Hopkins

November

MONDAY 20

The days come one at a time

TUESDAY 21

Courage is what has you bounce when you hit rock bottom

WEDNESDAY 22

Treasure the moments – they won't come again

The best six doctors anywhere
and no one can deny it –
are sunshine, water, rest and air,
exercise and diet.
Wayne Fields

I have chosen
to be happy
because it is
good for my
health.
Voltaire

**Happiness is the highest
form of health.**
Dalai Lama

You can't make footprints in the sands of time by sitting on the fence.
Bob Moawad

People with goals succeed because they know where they're going.
Earl Nightingale

The most important single ingredient in the formula of success is knowing how to get along with people.
Theodore Roosevelt

THURSDAY **23**

Spend time in quiet reflection

FRIDAY **24**

There is no reward for finding fault

SATURDAY **25**

Your intuition is powerful. Listen to it

SUNDAY **26**

When you have nothing to lose you have everything to gain

November

Far and away the best prize that life has to offer
is the chance to work at work worth doing.

Theodore Roosevelt

People who don't pursue their own dreams probably
won't encourage you to pursue yours.

Tim Grover

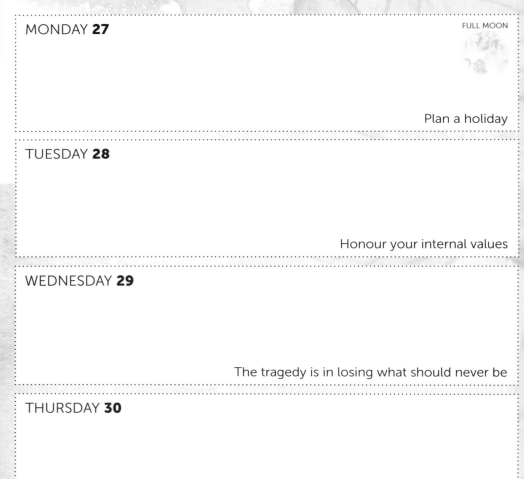

MONDAY 27

FULL MOON

Plan a holiday

TUESDAY 28

Honour your internal values

WEDNESDAY 29

The tragedy is in losing what should never be

THURSDAY 30

Go placidly amid the noise and haste

CHRISTMAS SHOPPING LIST

1. Buy a 2024 Get Up and Go Diary for all my friends.

2. Buy a Get Up and Go Gratitude Journal.

3. Buy a Get Up and Go Leadership Journal.

4. Buy a Daily Planner for...

Unless you stretch yourself beyond
that which you have already mastered,
you will not grow.

spriocanna

GOALS

NOLLAIG
DECEMBER

Dá fhada an lá tagann
an tráthnóna.

No matter how long the day,
the evening comes.

I dare you ...

When a new day dawns, dare to greet it with a smile.
When all you see is darkness, dare to be the first to shine a light.
When you see there is injustice, dare to be the first to condemn it.
When something seems difficult, dare to try anyway.
When life knocks you down, dare to get back up.
When there seems to be no hope, dare to find some.
When you're tired, dare to rest.
When times are tough, dare to be tougher.
When love has hurt you, dare to forgive.
When someone is hurt, dare to help them heal.
When another is lost, dare to guide them to find their way.
When an enemy has fallen, dare to offer a hand to lift them up.
When a friend is in trouble, dare to listen without judgement.
When you meet a stranger, dare to smile.
When life is great, dare to share it.
When life is a struggle, dare to admit it.
Dare to live the best life you can – today.
When today has ended, dare to trust that
tomorrow will give you another chance.

To believe .. .

... is to know that every day is a new beginning,
miracles happen and dreams do come true.
To believe is to know that angels dance in the clouds,
the sky is full of stardust, and the man in the moon is wise.
To believe is to know the value of a nurturing heart, the
innocence of a child's eyes, and the beauty of an ageing hand,
for it is through their teachings that we learn to love.
To believe is to find the strength and courage that lies within
us for when it is time to pick up the pieces and begin again.
To believe is to know we are not alone, that life is a gift
and this is our time to cherish it.
To believe is to know that wonderful surprises are waiting
to happen and all our hopes and dreams are within reach ...

... if only we believe.

11 PIECES OF WISDOM FROM DESMOND TUTU TO INSPIRE CHANGE MAKERS

1. If you are neutral in situations of injustice, you have chosen the side of the oppressor.
2. Without forgiveness, there can be no future for a relationship between individuals or within and between nations.
3. Religion is like a knife: you can either use it to cut bread, or stick in someone's back.
4. Resentment and anger are bad for your blood pressure and your digestion.
5. Do your little bit of good where you are; it's those little bits of good that overwhelm the world.
6. Hope is being able to see there is light despite all of the darkness.
7. Don't raise your voice, improve your argument.
8. If you want peace, don't talk to your friends, talk to your enemies.
9. Differences are not intended to separate, to alienate. We are different precisely in order to realise our need of one another.
10. Ubuntu… my humanity is caught up, is inextricably bound up, in what is yours.
11. Give a man a fish, feed him for a day. Teach a man to fish and he will feed himself for a lifetime.

We enhance the quality of our lives by elevating the quality of our thoughts.

In any moment of decision, the best thing you can do is the right thing, the next best thing you can do is the wrong thing. The worst thing you can do is the no thing.

Theodore Roosevelt

December

The way you see people is the way you treat them, and the way you treat them is what they become.

Goethe

This world demands the qualities of youth:
not a time of life but a state of mind,
a temper of the will,
a quality of the imagination,
a predominance of courage over timidity,
of the appetite for adventure over the life of ease.

Robert F Kennedy

FRIDAY 1

A loving heart is the truest wisdom

SATURDAY 2

Smile. It's good for your face

SUNDAY 3

I'm possible. What are you?

December

RECIPE FOR HAPPINESS

Two cups of patience.
One heart full of love.
Two handfuls of generosity.
A dash of laughter.
A heaped spoonful of understanding.
Sprinkle liberally with kindness.
Add a little faith and mix well.
Serve to everyone you meet.
Spread over a period of a lifetime.
Oh, and if it seems a wee bit under
cooked occasionally.
Remember to apply forgiveness!

Author unknown

A cloudy day is no match for a sunny disposition.

William Arthur Ward

Remember that the happiest people are not those getting more, but those giving more.

H Jackson Brown Jr

Do I contradict myself?
Very well, then I contradict myself,
I am large, I contain multitudes.

Walt Whitman

MONDAY **4**

Keep your curiosity alive

Be faithful in small things because it is in them that your strength lies.

Mother Teresa

TUESDAY 5

See criticism as constructive

Let your life lightly dance on the edges of time like dew on the tip of a leaf.

Tagore

There is a crack in everything. That's how the light gets in.

Leonard Cohen

The wrongdoer is more unfortunate than the one wronged.

Democritus

WEDNESDAY 6

Comparison is a pitfall

THURSDAY 7

Have the courage to bring forth what's in you

December

If you think you're a winner, you'll win.
If you dare to step out you'll succeed.
Believe in your heart,
Have a purpose to start,
Aim to help others in need.
Thoughts of faith must replace every doubt,
Words of courage and you cannot fail.
If you stumble and fall,
Rise and stand tall,
You determine the course that you sail.

Walter D Wintle

FRIDAY **8**

Be busy greening your own grass

SATURDAY **9**

Don't worry; be happy

SUNDAY **10**

Practice what you want to get good at

The heaviest load to carry is a bundle of grudges.

MONDAY 11

Use your stumbling block as a stepping stone

A well-developed sense of humour is the pole that adds balance to your steps as you walk the tightrope of life.
William Arthur Ward

TUESDAY 12

Don't dwell on failures

WEDNESDAY 13

You are part of all of it

THURSDAY 14

Don't underestimate yourself

December

FRIDAY **15**

Some days you may have to walk alone

What is not started today
is never finished tomorrow.
Fate leads those who follow it,
and drags those who resist.

Plutarch

May you have the gladness of Christmas which is hope;
the spirit of Christmas which is peace;
the heart of Christmas which is love.

Ada V Hendricks

SATURDAY **16**

Miracles can happen if you expect them

SUNDAY **17**

Let your mind be quiet enough to hear your heart

Have you tried everything you know to do?

REMEMBERED JOY

Don't grieve for me, for now I'm free!
I follow the plan God laid for me.
I saw His face, I heard His call,
I took His hand and left it all…
I could not stay another day,
To love, to laugh, to work or play;
Tasks left undone must stay that way.
And if my parting has left a void,
Then fill it with remembered joy.
A friendship shared, a laugh, a kiss…
Ah yes, these things I, too, shall miss.
My life's been full, I've savoured much:
Good times, good friends, a loved-
one's touch.
Perhaps my time seemed all too brief –
Don't shorten yours with undue grief.
Be not burdened with tears of sorrow,
Enjoy the sunshine of the morrow.

Anne Lindgren Davison

Ask yourself these three questions, and your answers will tell you who you are.

1. What do you believe in?
2. What do you hope for?
3. What do you love?

Instead of worrying about what people say of you, why not spend time trying to accomplish something they will admire.

Dale Carnegie

December

TUESDAY **19**

With the new day comes new thoughts and new strength

May the road rise to meet you
May the wind be always at your back
May the sun shine warm upon your face
And the rain fall softly on your fields.
And until we meet again, may God
hold you in the hollow of his hand.

Irish blessing

To be yourself in a world that is
constantly trying to make you
something else is the greatest
accomplishment.

Ralph Waldo Emerson

WEDNESDAY **20**

Do whatever brings you to life

THURSDAY **21**

What you have now is a result of what you did then

May your choices reflect your hopes, not your fears.

Nelson Mandela

A MOTHER'S LOVE

A mother's love is a blessing
No matter where you roam.
Keep her while she's living
You'll miss her when she's gone.
Love her as in childhood,
When feeble, old and grey.
For you'll never miss a mothers love
'Till she's buried beneath the clay.

Irish folksong

FRIDAY **22**

It's OK to ask questions

SATURDAY **23**

Some days you're the statue, others, the pigeon!

SUNDAY **24**

This too will pass

December

MONDAY 25 Christmas Day

What comes into the room when you show up?

TUESDAY 26 St Stephen's Day. Bank holiday

Value the contribution of others

WEDNESDAY 27 FULL MOON

A problem shared is a problem halved

Would you tell me please, which
way I ought to walk from here?"
That depends a good deal on where
you want to go" said the cat.
"I don't much care", said Alice.
"Then it does not matter which
way you walk" said the cat.

Alice in Wonderland

Gratitude is the fairest blossom that springs from the soul.

Ballou

THURSDAY 28

Everyone has a unique point of view

FRIDAY 29

Take the helicopter view

SATURDAY 30

All is well. This is life

SUNDAY 31 New Year's Eve

DESIDERATA

Go placidly amid the noise and haste, and remember what peace there may be in silence. As far as possible without surrender be on good terms with all persons. Speak your truth quietly and clearly, and listen to others, even the dull and ignorant; they too have their story.

Avoid loud and aggressive persons, they are vexations to the spirit. If you compare yourself with others, you may become vain and bitter; for always there will be greater and lesser persons than yourself. Enjoy your achievements as well as your plans. Keep interested in your own career, however humble; it is a real possession in the changing fortunes of time. Exercise caution in your business affairs; for the world is full of trickery. But let this not blind you to what virtue there is; many persons strive for high ideals; and everywhere life is full of heroism.

Be yourself. Especially, do not feign affection. Neither be cynical about love; for in the face of all aridity and disenchantment it is perennial as the grass. Take kindly the counsel of the years, gracefully surrendering the things of youth. Nurture strength of spirit to shield you in sudden misfortune. But do not distress yourself with imaginings. Many fears are born of fatigue and loneliness. Beyond a wholesome discipline, be gentle with yourself.

You are a child of the universe, no less than the trees and the stars; you have a right to be here. And whether or not it is clear to you, no doubt the universe is unfolding as it should. Therefore be at peace with God, whatever you conceive Him to be; and whatever your labours and aspirations, in the noisy confusion of life keep peace with your soul. With all its sham, drudgery and broken dreams, it is still a beautiful world. Be cheerful. Strive to be happy.

Max Ehrmann

2024

JANUARY

Sun	Mon	Tue	Wed	Thu	Fri	Sat
	1	2	3	4	5	6
7	8	9	10	11	12	13
14	15	16	17	18	19	20
21	22	23	24	25	26	27
28	29	30	31			

FEBRUARY

Sun	Mon	Tue	Wed	Thu	Fri	Sat
				1	2	3
4	5	6	7	8	9	10
11	12	13	14	15	16	17
18	19	20	21	22	23	24
25	26	27	28	29		

MARCH

Sun	Mon	Tue	Wed	Thu	Fri	Sat
					1	2
3	4	5	6	7	8	9
10	11	12	13	14	15	16
17	18	19	20	21	22	23
24	25	26	27	28	29	30
31						

APRIL

Sun	Mon	Tue	Wed	Thu	Fri	Sat
	1	2	3	4	5	6
7	8	9	10	11	12	13
14	15	16	17	18	19	20
21	22	23	24	25	26	27
28	29	30				

MAY

Sun	Mon	Tue	Wed	Thu	Fri	Sat
			1	2	3	4
5	6	7	8	9	10	11
12	13	14	15	16	17	18
19	20	21	22	23	24	25
26	27	28	29	30	31	

JUNE

Sun	Mon	Tue	Wed	Thu	Fri	Sat
						1
2	3	4	5	6	7	8
9	10	11	12	13	14	15
16	17	18	19	20	21	22
23	24	25	26	27	28	29
30						

JULY

Sun	Mon	Tue	Wed	Thu	Fri	Sat
	1	2	3	4	5	6
7	8	9	10	11	12	13
14	15	16	17	18	19	20
21	22	23	24	25	26	27
28	29	30	31			

AUGUST

Sun	Mon	Tue	Wed	Thu	Fri	Sat
				1	2	3
4	5	6	7	8	9	10
11	12	13	14	15	16	17
18	19	20	21	22	23	24
25	26	27	28	29	30	31

SEPTEMBER

Sun	Mon	Tue	Wed	Thu	Fri	Sat
1	2	3	4	5	6	7
8	9	10	11	12	13	14
15	16	17	18	19	20	21
22	23	24	25	26	27	28
29	30					

OCTOBER

Sun	Mon	Tue	Wed	Thu	Fri	Sat
		1	2	3	4	5
6	7	8	9	10	11	12
13	14	15	16	17	18	19
20	21	22	23	24	25	26
27	28	29	30	31		

NOVEMBER

Sun	Mon	Tue	Wed	Thu	Fri	Sat
					1	2
3	4	5	6	7	8	9
10	11	12	13	14	15	16
17	18	19	20	21	22	23
24	25	26	27	28	29	30

DECEMBER

Sun	Mon	Tue	Wed	Thu	Fri	Sat
1	2	3	4	5	6	7
8	9	10	11	12	13	14
15	16	17	18	19	20	21
22	23	24	25	26	27	28
29	30	31				

FOR MORE COPIES VISIT OUR WEBSITE
www.getupandgodiary.com
OR CONTACT US ON
info@getupandgodiary.com

Postal address: **Get Up and Go Publications Ltd, Unit 7A Cornhill Business Park, Ballyshannon, Co Donegal, Ireland F94 C4AA**

- -

For current prices, special offers and postal charges for your region, please refer to the website (www.getupandgodiary.com).

DIRECT ORDER FORM (please complete by ticking boxes)

PLEASE SEND ME:

The Irish Get Up and Go Diary (paperback), €12/£10 — Quantity ☐

The Irish Get Up and Go Diary (padded cover), €17.50/£15 — Quantity ☐

The Get Up and Go Diary (paperback), €12/£10 — Quantity ☐

Get Up and Go Diary for Busy Women (paperback), €12/£10 — Quantity ☐

Get Up and Go Diary for Busy Women (padded cover), €17.50/£15 — Quantity ☐

Daily Guide to Good Health and Wellbeing (paperback), €15/£13 — Quantity ☐

Get Up and Go Gratitude Journal (padded cover), €17.50/£15 — Quantity ☐

Get Up and Go Wallplanner (size: A1), €4/£4 — Quantity ☐

Total number of copies ☐

We encourage each reader to visit our website (www.getupandgodiary.com) for current prices, other products, special offers and postal charges for region.

I enclose cheque/postal order for (total amount including P+P): _____

Name: _____

Address: _____

Contact phone number: _____ Email: _____

For general enquiries or to pay by credit/debit card, please contact us on 071 9845938 *or* 085 1764297 (office hours).